A New Tune *for* Trumpet

CW00420335

Boston Music Company
part of The Music Sales Group
London/New York/Paris/Sydney/Copenhagen/Berlin/Madrid/Tokyo

Foreword

Since its appearance in the early 1930s, C. Paul Herfurth's original A Tune A Day series has become the most popular instrumental teaching method of all time. Countless music students have been set on their path by the clear, familiar, proven material, and the logical, sensibly-paced progression through the lessons within the book.

The teacher will find that the new books have been meticulously rewritten by experienced teachers: instrumental techniques and practices have been updated and the musical content has been completely overhauled.

The student will find clearly-presented, uncluttered material, with familiar tunes and a gentle introduction to the theoretical aspects of music. The books are now accompanied by audio CDs of examples and backing tracks to help the student develop a sense of rhythm, intonation and performance at an early stage.

As in the original books, tests are given following every five lessons. Teachers are encouraged to present these as an opportunity to ensure that the student has a good overview of the information studied up to this point.

The following extract from the foreword to the original edition remains as true today as the day it was written:

The value of learning to count aloud from the very beginning cannot be over-estimated. Only in this way can a pupil sense rhythm. Rhythm, one of the most essential elements of music, and usually conspicuous by its absence in amateur ensemble playing, is emphasised throughout.

Eventual success in mastering the instrument depends on regular and careful application to its technical demands. Daily practice should not extend beyond the limits of the player's physical endurance — the aim should be the gradual development of tone control alongside assured finger-work.

Music-making is a lifelong pleasure, and at its heart is a solid understanding of the principles of sound production and music theory. These books are designed to accompany the student on these crucial first steps: the rewards for study and practice are immediate and lasting.

Welcome to the world of music!

Special thanks to Pauline, Kelly Bea and Ross.
Thanks to Joe Atkins, David Carstairs, Paul Mayes, Timothy Jackson, Onyx Brass.
Thanks also to The Dulwich Music Shop.

Published by
Boston Music Company

Exclusive Distributors:
Music Sales Limited
8/9 Frith Street, London W1D 3JB, England.
Music Sales Corporation
257 Park Avenue South, New York, NY10010, USA.
Music Sales Pty Limited
120 Rothschild Avenue, Rosebery, NSW 2018, Australia.

This book © Copyright 2005 Boston Music Company,
a division of Music Sales Limited

Unauthorised reproduction of any part of this publication
by any means including photocopying is an infringement of copyright.

Edited by David Harrison
Music processed by Paul Ewers Music Design
Original compositions and arrangements by Brian Thomson
Cover and book designed by Chloë Alexander
Photography by Matthew Ward
Models: Chigozie Nri and Heidi Sutcliffe
Printed in the EU
Backing tracks by Guy Dagul
CD performance by Brian Thomson
CD recorded, mixed and mastered by Jonas Persson and John Rose

Your Guarantee of Quality

As publishers, we strive to produce every book to the highest commercial
standards. The music has been freshly engraved and the book has been
carefully designed to minimise awkward page turns and to make playing
from it a real pleasure. Throughout, the printing and binding have been
planned to ensure a sturdy, attractive publication which should give years
of enjoyment. If your copy fails to meet our high standards, please inform
us and we will gladly replace it.

www.musicsales.com

Contents

Rudiments of music

The stave

Music is written on a grid of five lines called a *stave*.

At the beginning of each stave is placed a special symbol called a *clef* to describe the approximate range of the instrument for which the music is written.

This example shows a *treble clef*, generally used for melody instruments.

The stave is divided into equal sections of time, called *bars* or *measures*, by *barlines*.

Note values

Different symbols are used to show the time value of *notes*, and each *note value* has an equivalent symbol for a rest, representing silence.

The **quaver** (or *eighth note*), often used to signify a half beat, is written with a solid head and a stem with a tail. The quaver rest is also shown.

The **crotchet** (or *quarter note*), often used to signify one beat, is written with a solid head and a stem. The crotchet rest is also shown.

The **minim** (or *half note*) is worth two crotchets. It is written with a hollow head and a stem. The minim rest is placed on the middle line.

The **semibreve** (or *whole note*) is worth two minims. It is written with a hollow head. The semibreve rest hangs from the fourth line.

Other note values

Note values can be increased by half by adding a dot after the note head. Here a minim and a crotchet are together worth a *dotted* minim.

Grouping quavers

Where two or more quavers follow each other, they can be joined by a *beam* from stem to stem.

Time signatures

The number of beats in a bar is determined by the *time signature*, a pair of numbers placed after the clef.
The upper number shows how many beats each bar contains, whilst the lower number indicates what kind of note value
is used to represent a single beat. This lower number is a fraction of a semibreve so that 4 represents crotchets
and 8 represents quavers.

C, for *common time*, is
another way to write $\frac{4}{4}$.

$\frac{6}{8}$ means six quavers to the bar.

$\frac{4}{4}$ means four crotchets to the bar.

$\frac{3}{4}$ means three crotchets to the bar.

Note names

Notes are named after the first seven letters of the alphabet and are written on lines or spaces on the stave,
according to pitch.

D   E   F   G   A   B   C   D   E   F   G

Accidentals

The pitch of a note can be altered up or down a half step (or *semitone*) by the use of sharp and flat symbols.
These temporary pitch changes are known as accidentals.

The *sharp* (♯) raises the pitch of a note.

The *natural* (♮) returns the note to its original pitch.

The *flat* (♭) lowers the pitch of a note.

Ledger lines

Ledger lines are used to extend the range of the stave for low or high notes.

C   B   A   G   A   B   C   D

Bar lines

Various different types of bar lines are used:

Double bar lines divide one section of music from another.

Final bar lines show the end of a piece of music.

Repeat marks show a section to be repeated.

Before you play:

The trumpet and accessories

Your complete trumpet outfit should include the following:

• Mouthpiece   • Valve oil

• Duster

• Pull-through

Setting up routine

Place the mouthpiece into the receiver and check that the valves and slides are all free – a few drops of oil on each valve every other day and a little grease on the slides occasionally will keep everything moving freely.

Remove the mouthpiece again before putting your instrument away.

Maintenance

Give your instrument a bath now and again – it will play much better if it is clean on the inside.

Strip the instrument down and immerse it in luke warm soapy water with a little disinfectant.

Pull the long brush through the leadpipe and all the slides. Rinse with luke warm water then dry it with a soft towel – remember to oil the valves and grease the slides afterwards.

Use a soft duster to keep your instrument clean and shiny.

Practice

Playing any musical instrument is a physical skill, and repetition is necessary to develop your mental and muscular skills. The three most important things to remember about practice are:

1. Practise until you can't get something wrong, rather than just until you get it right once; this way you are less likely to get it wrong next time.

2. It is much better to practise "little and often" rather than in one long session once a week. A daily practice routine of 15 or 20 minutes is ideal.

3. Never finish a practice session without having got at least one thing better than it was when you started.

1. **Breathing using the diaphragm**
2. **Posture**
3. **Formation of the mouth shape (embouchure)**
4. **Buzzing on the mouthpiece**
5. **Making a sound on the instrument**

Breathing

A relaxed, controlled posture is essential for comfort and correct breathing.

When breathing in and out, always use your diaphragm. This is a large muscular membrane underneath your rib cage which causes your stomach to go *out* when breathing in and to go *in* when breathing out.

You will be able to control your breathing far more effectively using your diaphragm than if you were to breathe with the *intercostal* muscles high up in your chest.

Exercise 1:

Count a steady beat in your head as you inhale through your nose then exhale naturally through your mouth. Feel the air going deep down into your lungs.

in 2 3 4   out 2 3 4   in 2 3 4   out 2 3 4   in 2 3 4   out 2 3 4   in 2 3 4   out 2 3 4

All good trumpet players take a deep breath every time they play.

Posture

Stand up tall with your feet planted shoulder width apart.

Keep this posture as you raise the trumpet to playing position, allowing your elbows to move forward and away from your body. Keep the shoulders relaxed.

Hold the weight of the trumpet with the left hand while keeping the right hand relaxed for a good valve technique.

Wrap your **left hand** around the valves using one finger to operate the 3rd valve slide (the slide with the ring mounted above it). Depending on the size of your hand, either the ring finger or little finger will fit into the ring.

Embouchure

Follow this routine to set up your embouchure correctly.

- Bite your teeth together then say **Too**
  (your tongue stays behind your teeth)

- Now open your teeth slightly (just enough to
  let some air through)

- Inhale as you say **Emmmm** (this compresses
  your lips – hold the "mmm")

- Blow... As you spit **Tffff**
  (enjoy blowing raspberries!)

*Try moistening your
lips before you play to
help free the "buzz".*

Placing the mouthpiece

The mouthpiece should ideally be placed in the centre
with half on the upper lips and half on the lower lips.

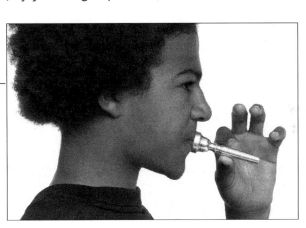

Buzzing on the mouthpiece

Try this exercise using only the mouthpiece.

Exercise 2:

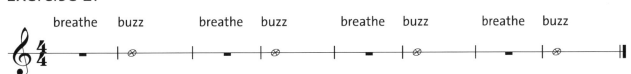

breathe   buzz   breathe   buzz   breathe   buzz   breathe   buzz

3-4

Listen to CD tracks 3 and 4. Try to home in on one of these notes while "buzzing" this exercise.
Aim for whichever note feels more comfortable.
Now, place the mouthpiece in the trumpet and do exactly the same.

Exercise 3:

breathe   Tfff...   breathe   Tfff...   breathe   Tfff...   breathe   Tfff...

Take a deep breath and enjoy the sound!
Practise this many times.

You will naturally play either a **G** or a **C**.

> ### NOTE
> If your preferred note is **G** proceed to
> lesson **1G** on page 12.
> If you are more comfortable
> playing a **C** begin with lesson **1C** on page 10.

Lesson 1C goals:

1. Tonguing
2. The notes C and D
3. Counting while playing: crotchets, minims and semibreves
4. Little C & D march

The note C

First practise playing a nice steady **C**.

Breathe and blow **Tffff**

Exercise 1:

Listen to the sound

Breath in while counting 4 beats then play for 4 beats and so on.

Now lets try tonguing a few notes. Say **Too** for each note, like so:

Exercise 2:

Take a deep breath and blow.

Try to feel a regular pulse as you play.

Exercise 3:

Exercise 4:

Exercise 5:

The note D

Now do exactly the same with the note **D**.

D is played using the 1st & 3rd valves.

Raise the trumpet to your lips – and try not to stoop!

Exercise 6:

Exercise 7: Take a deep breath and blow.

Now try these tunes using C and D.

Tune 1:

Tune 2:

Tune 3:

Play this exercise by tonguing only the first note of each group.

Little C & D March: Take a deep breath and blow.

5–6

Now proceed to Lesson **2C** on page 14.

goals:

1. Tonguing
2. The notes G and F

3. Counting while playing: crotchets, minims and semibreves
4. Little F & G march

The note G

First practise playing a nice steady **G**.

Breathe and blow **Tffff**

Exercise 1:

Listen to the sound

Breath in while counting 4 beats then play for 4 beats and so on.

Now lets try tonguing a few notes. Say **Too** for each note, like so:

Exercise 2:

Take a deep breath and blow.

Try to feel a regular pulse as you play.

Exercise 3:

Exercise 4:

Exercise 5:

The note F

Now do exactly the same with the note **F**.

F is played using the 1st valve.

*Raise the trumpet
to your lips – and
try not to stoop!*

Exercise 6:

Exercise 7: Take a deep breath and blow.

Now try these tunes using F and G.

Tune 1:

Tune 2:

Tune 3:

Play this exercise by tonguing only the first note of each group.

Little F & G March: Take a deep breath and blow.

7●8

Now proceed to Lesson **2G** on page 15.

13

goals:

1. The notes E & F

The note E

The note E is played using the 1st & 2nd valves.

The note F

The note F is played using the 1st valve.

Exercise 1: Take a deep breath and blow.

Exercise 2:

Duet

9

Try to learn both parts.

Now work through lessons **1G** and **2G** before playing the Pieces for Lesson 2.

1. The notes E & D

The note E

The note E is played using the 1st & 2nd valves.

The note D

The note D is played using the 1st & 3rd valves.

Exercise 1: Take a deep breath and blow.

Exercise 2:

Duet

Try to learn both parts.

Now work through lessons **1C** and **2C** before playing the pieces for Lesson 2.

Pieces for Lesson 2

Gheta Sea

Oats And Beans

11-12 ## *Lightly Row*

13 ## *Medieval Dance*

Try this canon with your teacher. The second player begins a bar after the first.
Notice the pause (or *fermata*) sign ⌢ . This means that the note is held, making it a little longer than
is written. The second player should finish on the pause in the penultimate bar.

Canon

Au Clair de la Lune

14⊝15

Going Cuckoo

Pia-Pia-Piano

goals:

1. Tied notes and slurred notes

Tied notes

So far we have tongued all our notes. Let's now introduce the "tie" and the "slur".

Two notes of the same pitch can be joined together by *tying* them with a curved line.

This new note is held for the combined value of both notes, and the note can be held into the next bar.

Hold this note for 3 beats.

Hold the middle note for 2 beats.

Tongue Tied

Slurred notes

To play smoothly between different notes we *slur* from one to the next without using the tongue and using only the valves.

Ice Slur

Oats And Beans

Take care to spot which notes are *tied* and which ones are *slurred*.

Lightly Row

Pieces for Lesson 3

Upidee Duet

When The Saints Go Marching In

Up The Old Vic

Lesson 4

goals:

1. **Tongue & fingers coordination**
2. **Time signatures**
3. **Slurred notes**
4. **Dotted notes**

Team talk

The tongue and fingers need to work together as a team, and to achieve smooth changes between notes it helps to move the valves quickly.

In the following exercises, *bang down* the valves as you tongue the notes.

Exercise 1:

1st time tongued, 2nd time slurred

Try the same exercise again with the slurs. Move the valves quickly to make it nice and smooth.

Gliding

Ice Is Nice

1st time tongued, 2nd time slurred

Dotted Notes

A dot placed to the right of a note multiplies its duration by half as much again.

For example both notes here have the same duration.

> ## THINK!
>
> Take a deep breath and blow through the slurs.
> Are you standing up straight?
> Don't slouch!

Time signatures

Everything you have played so far has had a **time signature** of four beats to every bar:

Many pieces, however, contain three beats per bar. This means that the counting will be:

Waltzes always use this time signature.

Pieces for Lesson 4

Floating Along

Be sure to count in time.

Dance

Sailing Along Duet

Learn both parts for this piece. Keep a steady beat.

Lesson 5 goals:

1. **Lip slur**
2. **Vowel sounds**
3. **The notes A and B**
4. **Dynamics**

Lip slurs and vowel sounds

So far you have *slurred* between two notes using the valves.

We can also *lip slur* between two notes that use the same valves.
To help change the note it is useful to blow using vowel sounds.

For example, say **ah** then **eee** – feel the difference in the level of your tongue?
We use these vowel sounds and many in between to help our flexibility on the instrument.

Using the sounds **too – ah** and **ah – hoo** try these exercises on the mouthpiece only as well as on the trumpet.

Exercise 1:

Remember to take a deep breath before blowing.

On the way down from G to C, move quickly between **oo – ah** and relax your lips slightly to achieve a nice clean lip slur.

Repeat these many times until it feels comfortable

On the way up you'll need a bit of a push of air from your diaphragm.
Say **hoo** – feel where that push of air comes from? Think **tah – hoo** on the way up.

Exercise 2:

Blow through the lip slur

On the way up from C to G, move quickly between **ah – hoo** and compress your lips slightly to achieve a nice clean lip slur.

Exercise 3:

Once this is comfortable, try the same exercise with the 2nd valve down.

You can play these exercises using any valve combination.
Ask your teacher to demonstrate!

The note A

The note A is played using the 1st & 2nd valves.

The note B

The note B is played using the 2nd valve in both the upper and lower registers.

Extending range to A & B

Play these exercises first time tongued and second time all slurred.

Blow through the crescendos to give you some power for the higher notes.

Exercise 4:

1st time tongued, 2nd time slurred

Exercise 5:

1st time tongued, 2nd time slurred

Dynamics

To play at a loud dynamic (f – *forte*) you must *blow* the air faster through the instrument, and to play quietly (p – *piano*) blow gently while keeping some air support from your diaphragm.

Crescendo means gradually get louder, also shown as ![crescendo]

Diminuendo means gradually get quieter, also shown as ![diminuendo]

Pieces for Lesson 5

Call And Response

Play this fun piece with another player.

Twinkle Twinkle

26-27 ## Joshua Fought The Battle Of Jericho

Crusaders' Hymn

Pieces for Lesson 5

Steal Away

Happy Days

Try to play this one a little quicker and emphasise the beginning of each tied note to achieve a lively feel.

Blue Tuesday Duet

Learn both parts.

1. Note duration

On the stave below, draw notes of the indicated duration:

(4)

2. Rests

On the stave below, draw rests of the indicated duration:

(4)

3. Notes

On the stave below, draw the following notes as minims:

G, B, E, C, A, D and **F**

(4)

4. Identity parade

Identify the following elements in this piece of music:

Crotchet, Bar line, Time signature, Crotchet rest, Tied note, Treble clef, Semibreve, Dotted minim

(8)

5. Bars

Draw bar lines on this stave where they are needed

(5)

Total (25)

warm up:

As with any physical activity it is a good idea to *warm up* each day with a few simple exercises to loosen up the muscles, get the blood flowing and focus the mind.

Warming up helps to make each practise session more productive.

Develop a new good habit by warming up for five minutes each day with some simple exercises.

Ask your teacher for good advice on how to warm up. Here are some exercises to try:

1. Mouthpiece buzzing

Buzz a few long steady notes and a few slides to free up the buzz.

2. Long notes

Play a few long notes and listen to the sound. Is it clear?

Is it a beautiful sound? Imagine you are blowing warm air into the trumpet. Try standing at the window and steam it up by blowing warm air onto it. Feel how this opens up your throat?

3. Lip slurs

4. Tonguing (Production)

Try to get good clean starts to each note.

GOOD BRASS HABITS

- Always take a deep breath, even to play a quiet note
- Breath in time, being ready to blow when the note should begin
- Stand or sit with good posture: feet planted, shoulders down, back off the chair
- Raise the trumpet to your lips and try not to stoop
- Blow warm air, keeping your throat open

Lesson 6 goals:

1. The notes C, E♭ and B♭
2. C major scale
3. D.C. al Fine

The note C

You have already met the note C in the lower octave. Use the same fingering for the upper octave (open valves).

The scale of C major

A scale is a series of notes that move up or down by step from one note to the same note an octave higher or lower.

The note E♭

The note E♭ is played using the 2nd & 3rd valves.

The note B♭

The note B♭ is played using the 1st valve.

Pieces for Lesson 6

Skye Boat Song

This beautiful melody has *D.C. al Fine* written at the end. This means that you play all the way through then go back to the beginning and play through again until you see "Fine".

Scarborough Fair Duet

Joshua Fought The Battle Of Jericho

goals:

1. Combine the up and down lip slur

Here are some exercises to help you play lip slurs in both directions.

Move quickly between the vowel sounds **ooo** and **ah** as you compress and relax your lips.

Blow more air (**hoo**) as you go higher.

Exercise 1:

Repeat these until they become comfortable

Exercise 2:

Blow through the slur

Now try these again using different valve combinations.

Now move down in semitones, starting on F♯ (2nd valve), then F (1st valve) and finally E (1st & 2nd valve).

Ask your teacher to demonstrate these.

Exercise 3:

Blow the vowel sounds to help push the "lip slurs" up and down.

GOOD BRASS HABITS

Practise lip slurs slowly at first.
Blow through the changes to make
them clean and smooth

Pieces for Lesson 7

When The Saints Go Marching In

Yankee Doodle

Medieval Dance

Swap parts on the repeat

Canon The Bells

The 2nd player begins one bar later and finishes on the first pause. Play this one quickly – think in two minim beats to the bar.

goals:

1. **Warm up**
2. **The note F♯**
3. **Key of G major**

The note F♯

Don't forget to warm up.

Five minutes on these simple exercises will help you develop your playing in the right way and make your practice sessions more productive.

The note F♯ is played using the 2nd valve.

Exercise 1:

A sharp (♯) raises the note by a semitone and a flat (♭) lowers the note by a semitone.

A natural (♮) cancels out the effect of a sharp or a flat, simply play a natural note.

In this next exercise take care to play the correct sharp, flat or natural notes.

Exercise 2:

Key signatures

If you try to sing a simple tune such as *Somewhere Over The Rainbow*, you may find you can't reach the high notes without really straining. The solution is to start the piece a little lower.

This time, you may be able to sing the high notes more comfortably.

You are now singing in a different *key*.

There are many different keys in music, each of which needs its own set of notes.

The key of C major is easy as it requires no sharps or flats.

The key of G major has 1 sharp (F♯). Notice the sharp sign (♯) at the beginning of the stave – this means that every F throughout this piece is played as an F♯.

Exercise 3:

3rd Valve

Bell

Water Key

3rd Valve Slide   Left Hand Finger Ring   Tuning Slide

Transposition

The Bb trumpet and cornet sound a r...

Rule: **Written C sounds Bb**

Written:

Sounds:

Pitch System

The letter names which appear in th...

octave as well as the name of each ...

nd below the written pitch.

g chart indicate the relative
own below.

Mouthpiece　　　　　　Leadpipe　　　　　　　　　1st Valve　　　2nd Valve

1st Valve Slide　　　2nd Valve Slide

Pieces for Lesson 8

Au Clair de la Lune Duet

Jingle Bells

goals:

1. **Quavers, 2/4 time signature & Common time**

2. **Anacrusis (Up beat)**

Quavers

Quavers are half the length of crotchets so we play two quavers in the time of one crotchet.

And similarly the time signature of $\frac{2}{4}$ has half as many beats as $\frac{4}{4}$. Therefore the same melody can be played in $\frac{2}{4}$ using quavers as in $\frac{4}{4}$ using crotchets.

The $\mathbf{C}$ at the start is an alternative way of writing the time signature $\frac{4}{4}$ and is called '**Common time**'.

Exercise 1:

Exercise 2:

Exercise 3:

Exercise 4:

Take care with the following exercise, note the *key signature* and *time signature*.

THINK!

Are you practising properly?
Remember, a little each day...
Always warm up before you practise.
Your session will be more productive therefore you will progress at a quicker rate.

Pieces for Lesson 9

Abide With Me

Long, Long Ago

arranged Mayes

Anacrusis (up beat)

Sometimes a piece of music doesn't begin with a whole bar. The next piece begins with a single beat representing the last beat of a bar. This short bar (called an up beat or *anacrusis*) is balanced by another short bar at the end. The two short bars add up to a whole bar.

Remember – the symbol ⌢ above the last note in this next piece is called a **pause**.
It means you should hold the note on for longer than its actual value of 3 beats.

Oh Come All Ye Faithful

Yankee Doodle

35

Lesson 10 goals:

1. **Tonguing exercises**
2. **The upper note D**
3. **Key of F major**
4. **More Dynamics**

Tonguing exercises

Don't forget to warm up.

Try these exercises a little quicker each time.

Gradually speed them up without losing the quality of your note production.

Exercise 1:

Practise coordinating the valves and the tongue at gradually quicker tempos.

Exercise 2:

Key of F major

Notice that the key of F major has one flat (B♭), so all the Bs throughout this piece are played as B♭s.

Exercise 3:

The upper note D

The upper note D is played using the 1st valve.

Exercise 4:

More dynamics

So far you have only learned two dynamics, soft ($\boldsymbol{p}$) and loud ($\boldsymbol{f}$). The letter $\boldsymbol{m}$ can be used in combination with $\boldsymbol{p}$ and $\boldsymbol{f}$ to create other dynamics: $\boldsymbol{mp}$ (*mezzo piano*) means moderately soft and $\boldsymbol{mf}$ (*mezzo forte*) means moderately loud. The Italian word *mezzo* means literally 'half'.

Exercise 5:

Play these notes with the indicated dynamics.

Pieces for Lesson 10

Hark! The Herald Angels Sing

Pieces for Lesson 10

46-47
Auld Lang Syne

48-49
In Dulci Jubilo

Jubilant

Listen to track 2 on the CD. Learn this next tune and you can play along at the beginning, on the repeat and during the final refrain of the recording.

2
Prince Of Denmark's March

test: *for* Lessons 6 to 10

1. Note duration

On the stave below, draw notes of the indicated duration:

I quaver   2 beats-worth of quavers   dotted crotchet   a note that lasts for 5 quavers

(4)

2. Scale

On the stave below, draw the G major scale including the correct key signature:

(4)

3. Time signatures

Write in the correct time signature at the beginning of each bar:

(6)

4. Dynamics

What are the Italian words for:

Moderately loud _____

Moderately quiet _____

(4)

5. Performance

Choose your favourite piece so far and **perform** it to an audience of friends, family or your teacher.

(7)

Total **(25)**

Lesson 11 goals:

1. The note G♯
2. Minor keys

3. A minor scales
4. Staccato and tenuto tonguing

The note G♯

We play the note G♯ using the 2nd and 3rd valves.

Exercise 1:

Remember – in any bar, a note that has been flattened or sharpened will remain so throughout the bar unless indicated

Minor keys and minor scales

You have already played many cheerful melodies in different major keys.

To play something that sounds sad or melancholic a **minor** key would more often be used.

C major and A minor share the same key signature since they are based on the same range of notes.

For this reason we call them *relatives* – A minor is the *relative* minor of C major.

All major keys have a relative minor key and there are two types of minor scale – melodic and harmonic.

Exercise 2:

A melodic minor   *think!*   *think!*

A harmonic minor   *think!*   *think!*

In the *melodic minor scale* the notes change on the way down whereas they remain the *same both ways* in the *harmonic minor scale*.

Exercise 3:

Staccato & tenuto tonguing

Staccato tonguing means playing very short notes. Look out for the dot above or below the note head, and
Tenuto means playing long, full length notes. Look out for the line.

Exercise 4:

Play this exercise again using *tenuto* tonguing.

Try tonguing **doo doo doo** to achieve long, full notes and nice smooth changes.

Pieces for Lesson 11

Theme From Symphony No.9   Beethoven

Oh! Susannah

While Shepherds Watched Their Flocks

Gently

Lesson 12

goals:

1. **The note C♯**
2. **Key of D major**
3. **D major scale**

Don't forget to warm up.

The note bottom C♯

We play the note bottom C♯ using all 3 valves.

The note upper C♯

We play the upper C♯ on 1st & 2nd valves.

The scale of D major

Notice that the key of D major has two sharps (F♯ & C♯), so all the Fs and Cs will be sharp throughout the piece.

Exercise 1:

> **TALKING ITALIAN**
>
> *Dolce* means sweet.
> Play the lullaby on the following page sweetly.

Pieces for Lesson 12

Deck The Halls

Lullaby

Joy To The World

goals:

1. **Triplets**
2. **6/8 time signature**

Triplets & 6/8 time signature

So far we have had two quavers to each crotchet. Let's have some fun with three.

These are called **triplets** since we play three notes to every beat like so:

Exercise 1:

The 3 above each group of notes tells us to play 3 notes in each beat.

The same rhythm could also be written like this:

Exercise 2:

Think: 1 & a 2 & a 1 & a 2 & a etc...

$\frac{6}{8}$ means we have six quavers in each bar. Think of it as two beats in the bar, two groups of three.

Pieces for Lesson 13

Mexican Hat Dance

Row, Row, Row Your Boat

Pieces for Lesson 13

Mulberry Bush

57–58

Spanish Dance

59–60

Lean on the tied notes to give this one some Spanish flavour.

On Christmas Night

1. **Key of B♭ major**
2. **Scale of B♭ major**
3. **Introduction to swing quavers**
4. **D.S. al Fine**

Let's have some more fun with some jazz-style triplets.

Jazzy tunes have a natural triplet rhythm with a 'swinging' feel, like so:

Exercise 1:

Exercise 2:

The same piece would more often be written like this, with "Swing" written above:

Key of B♭

Notice that the key of B♭ has two flats (B♭ and E♭), so all the Bs throughout this piece are played as B♭s, and all the Es are E♭s.

> ### REMEMBER!
>
> B♭ is played with the 1st valve, and E♭ is played with the 2nd and 3rd valves.

The scale of B♭ major

Pieces for Lesson 14

Blue Bells Of Scotland

Don't forget to warm up!

DS al Fine means go back to the sign (𝄋) and play again until *Fine* (end).

Jingle Bells – Jazz Style

Blow The Boogie Woogie

Believe Me If All Those Endearing Young Charms

Lesson 15

goals:

1. **Lip slurs up to middle C**
2. **Lip flexibilities using all 7 valve combinations**

Lip Slurs

So far we have looked at lip slurs from C to G and below. Now lets try slurring using the next harmonic up.

Exercise 1:

Blow **too** – **hee**.

Feel what happens to your tongue?
And listen to the air speed increase!

Do exactly the same on the trumpet!

Exercise 2:

Let's begin with E on 1&2 and lip slur up to A. Use a slightly higher vowel sound for this one.

Always remember to take a deep breath.

Blow through the slur.

Push the note up by blowing **too** – **hee** as you compress your lips slightly.

Exercise 3:

Lip flexibilities

Practise lip flexibilities going up and down all seven combinations.

Practise these exercises using all seven valve positions:

These are called **lip flexibilities**.

Pieces for Lesson 15

Skating

Think **too** – **hee** at the beginning of this one to push up the lip slur.

Home On The Range

67—68

The First Noël

69—70

Notice the dynamic markings in this next piece. Try to grade the dynamics so that the piece becomes progressively louder, saving some strength for the final 4 bars.

test: *for* Lessons 11 to 15

1. Key signatures

On the stave below, draw the correct key signatures for:

G major   F major   A minor   A major   C major

(4)

2. Dots

Simplify the music on the left using dots to get rid of the ties

(4)

3. Notes

Write out the following notes with the correct fingering above each note

G♯, B♭, F♯, D, C♯, A

(6)

4. Terms

What do the following terms mean:

Fermata _____   Diminuendo _____

Legato _____   Mezzo forte _____

Piano _____   Staccato _____

(6)

5. Scale

Write out and play the A melodic minor scale on the stave below

(5)

Total (25)

50

warm up:

Hopefully by now you will be in the habit of warming up before each practice session.

Warming up each day will make your practice sessions more productive, help you develop some fundamental techniques for good brass playing, develop strength and stamina which will help you to play longer, louder and higher, and encourage a faster rate of progress.

It is a good idea to stick to one warm up for a period of time to allow these exercises to develop your muscles in a certain way.

It is also a good idea to change your warm up from time to time to encourage the development of new techniques to add interest.

Here are a few more exercises to add to your warm up routine:

1. Lip flexibilities

Repeat these many times using different valve combinations

Lip slurs develop flexibility and strengthen the muscles around your embouchure.

Remember to make use of vowel sounds

2. Tongue and valve coordination

Practise this exercise progressively quicker to develop a good rapport between the valves and fingers.

Practise this exercise both tongued and slurred

3. Speed tonguing

Practise this type of pattern tonguing as quickly as you can – try to play a little quicker each day.
You will soon develop a super fast tongue!

Practise this pattern on any note you like

goals:

1. Intervals and vowel sounds
2. Arpeggios

You will have seen how helpful vowel sounds can be to make lip flexibilities easier.
The same technique can be applied to playing all kinds of intervals, big and small.

Exercise 1:

Play the upper note *louder* and *crescendo* through the lower note to generate some extra power for the upper note.

Exercise 2:

Experiment with the "vowel sounds" to find which ones help you leap from note to note.

Blow through the crescendo

Arpeggios

An *arpeggio* is a short "fanfare" based on the notes that form the chord of a particular key.

Exercise 3: the C major arpeggio

Practise using your vowel sound technique to help leap up and down the arpeggios.

Exercise 4:

Pieces for Lesson 16

Hop, Skip & Jump

Jumping Beans

Swing Low, Sweet Chariot

Spiritual

71-72

goals:

1. **Articulation**
2. **Note shape**

Refresh your memory and learn some new ways to articulate notes on the trumpet.

Articulation

Articulation describes the way a note is played.

For example, a note can be short or long, and can be played with a hard or soft *attack* .

Exercise 1: *Staccato*

The dot means that each note should be played short. This is called **staccato**, which literally means 'detached'. Simply blow a short, sharp burst of air as you say **too**.

Exercise 2: *Accent*

The *accent* indicates that each note should be given a harder attack.

It helps to push a little extra air into each note as well as sharpening your **too**.

Exercise 3: *Soft tonguing*

To articulate softly try using **doo** rather than **too**. Feel how your tongue is slightly further back in the mouth? To help make an even softer tonguing, imagine that the air starts the note with **hoo** then add a soft **doo** on top.

Exercise 4: *Tenuto* and *detached* notes

The line indicates that the notes should be played to their full length.

This is called *tenuto*, literally meaning 'held'. Play these notes with a continuous airstream, blowing from one note into the next.

Where a line and a dot are used together, the note should be played detached, but not as short as *staccato*, and should be given emphasis. Think of them as notes that *bounce*. Again, a little push of air helps each one. Put **too** and **hoo** together.

Note shape

The shape of the start of each note is also very important to good trumpet playing.

Try to avoid the "wa – wa" effect:

Exercise 5:

Practise starting notes positively like this:

Practise this exercise softly and loudly

Pieces for Lesson 17

Mango Walk

73 – 74

Can Can

Lesson 18

goals:

1. The notes E and E♭
2. E♭ major
3. Lip flexibilities up to E

The note E

E above middle C is part of the open harmonic range, so this note is played on open valves.

The note E♭

This E♭ is played using the 2nd valve.

The scale and arpeggio of E♭ major

Notice that the key of E♭ major has 3 flats – B♭, E♭ and A♭.

This means that every B, E and A will be flat throughout the piece.

Here are some more lip flexibilities.

Hopefully by now you are playing lip slurs up to middle C in your warm up. Take these a step further now by using the next harmonic up. Begin with G on 1 & 3 and work up from there.

Exercise 1:

Practise these slowly at first using the vowel sounds **te** and **eee** and a little push of air with **hee** to help you blow these notes up and down.

Remember where **hoo** comes from in your stomach – give that same push with **hee**.

Compress your lips slightly on the way up and relax again on the way down.

Continue up the valve sequence to C on open valves.

56

Exercise 2:

Blow through the lip slur. Give a little push from your belly on the way up.

Think **too** – **eh** – **oo** – **o** – **oo** then **teh** – **ee** – **eh** – **oo** – **eh** as you go higher.

Use vowel sounds to
help push the lip slurs
up and down

Pieces for Lesson 18

When The Saints Go Marching In (E♭)

Home Sweet Home

goals:

1. **The note upper F**
2. **Range building**

The note upper F

The note F is played using the same fingering in both octaves: 1st valve.

Range building

Trumpet melodies often contain high notes, and this requires strength and stamina.

This exercise develops control of the airstream: experiment with the vowel sounds studied so far to see what works best, and crescendo through each phrase.

Exercise 1:

Blow through the slur

Practise this exercise often and add another note on top as it becomes easier.

Pieces for Lesson 19

76–77

Blue Skies

Reflective

Winding Up

goals:

1. **Musical expression**
2. **D minor scales and arpeggio**
3. **Extreme dynamics**

Musical expression

The trumpet can be a very expressive instrument and there are many ways to give meaning to the music.

To play in a lyrical style we can use a sensitive mixture of all the musical expressions we have learned so far.
Use more varied combinations of dynamics, slurs, tempos and articulation to express your musical ideas.

Pieces for Lesson 20

Try to give these two contrasting pieces their own individual character.
Sostenuto means sustained – try to play nice long phrases and gently *crescendo* and *diminuendo* where marked. Give the Rondo some gusto!

From *The Unfinished Symphony*
Schubert

Rondo from Horn Concerto No.4
Mozart

Let's hear the hunting horns calling!

D minor scales and arpeggio

F major and D minor are *relatives* since they share the same key signature.

Exercise 1:

D melodic minor

Exercise 2:

D harmonic minor

Exercise 3:

D minor arpeggio

Extreme Dynamics

Practise these simple exercises to develop strength and control for louder and softer dynamics. *ff* means *double forte* – even louder than forte, and **pp** means *double piano* – even softer than piano.
We need to control the dynamics at both extremes.

Don't blow so loud that it distorts the sound and not so soft that the sound disappears completely.

Exercise 4:

Practise these exercises using different notes to help you develop good dynamic control over your full register.

Exercise 5:

Pieces for Lesson 20

Greensleeves

79 ## *Got The Blues*

1. Articulations

Play the following well-known piece taking care to make all the articulations.

Try to distinguish between each different articulation in your performance.

(6)

2. New keys

Return to page 19 and, using your knowledge of scales and key signatures,

play *When The Saints Go Marching In* in two other major keys of your choice.

(6)

3. Breath control

Play this note with a steady tone, controlling your breath at all times.

You will score one mark (up to a maximum of five) for every three seconds held.

(5)

4. Dynamics

Put these dynamic marks in the correct order from softest to loudest

mf   *p*   *ff*   *mp*   *pp*   *f*

(3)

5. Arpeggios

Play the arpeggios of the following keys:

B♭ major   **D major**   **F major**   **A minor**   **E♭ major**

(5)

Total (25)

CD backing tracks

1   Tuning note B♭
2   Virtuoso Performance
3   Buzzing (C) *demonstration*
4   Buzzing (G) *demonstration*
5   Little C & D March *demonstration*
6   Little C & D March *backing only*
7   Little F & G March *demonstration*
8   Little F & G March *backing only*
9   C *duet*
10 G *duet*
11 Lightly Row *demonstration*
12 Lightly Row *backing only*
13 Medieval Dance *duet*
14 Au Clair de la Lune *demonstration*
15 Au Clair de la Lune *backing only*
16 Upidee *duet*
17 When The Saints Go Marching In *demonstration*
18 When The Saints Go Marching In *backing only*
19 Up The Old Vic *demonstration*
20 Up The Old Vic *backing only*
21 Floating Along *demonstration*
22 Floating Along *backing only*
23 Dance *demonstration*
24 Dance *backing only*
25 Sailing Along *duet*
26 Joshua Fought The Battle Of Jericho *demonstration*
27 Joshua Fought The Battle Of Jericho *backing only*
28 Steal Away *demonstration*
29 Steal Away *backing only*
30 Blue Tuesday *duet*
31 Skye Boat Song *demonstration*
32 Skye Boat Song *backing only*
33 Scarborough Fair *duet*

34 When The Saints Go Marching In *demonstration*
35 When The Saints Go Marching In *backing only*
36 Medieval Dance *duet backing only*
37 Au Clair de la Lune *duet*
38 Long Long Ago *demonstration*
39 Long Long Ago *backing only*
40 O Come All Ye Faithful *demonstration*
41 O Come All Ye Faithful *backing only*
42 Yankee Doodle *demonstration*
43 Yankee Doodle *backing only*
44 Hark! The Herald Angels Sing *demonstration*
45 Hark! The Herald Angels Sing *backing only*
46 Auld Lang Syne *demonstration*
47 Auld Lang Syne *backing only*
48 In Dulci Jubilo *demonstration*
49 In Dulci Jubilo *backing only*
50 Oh! Susannah *demonstration*
51 Oh! Susannah *backing only*
52 Deck The Halls *demonstration*
53 Deck The Halls *backing only*
54 Lullaby *duet*
55 Joy To The World *demonstration*
56 Joy To The World *backing only*
57 Mulberry Bush *demonstration*
58 Mulberry Bush *backing only*
59 Spanish Dance *demonstration*
60 Spanish Dance *backing only*
61 Jingle Bells – Jazz Style *demonstration*
62 Jingle Bells – Jazz Style *backing only*

63 Blow The Boogie Woogie *demonstration*
64 Blow The Boogie Woogie *backing only*
65 Believe Me If *demonstration*
66 Believe Me If *backing only*
67 Home On The Range *demonstration*
68 Home On The Range *backing only*
69 The First Noel *demonstration*
70 The First Noel *backing only*
71 Swing Low, Sweet Chariot *demonstration*
72 Swing Low, Sweet Chariot *backing only*
73 Mango Walk *demonstration*
74 Mango Walk *backing only*
75 Home Sweet Home *duet*
76 Blue Skies *demonstration*
77 Blue Skies *backing only*
78 Winding Up *trio*
79 Got The Blues *trio*

How to use the CD

The tuning note on track one is a concert B♭, which sounds C on the trumpet.

After track 2, which gives an idea of how the trumpet can sound, the backing tracks are listed in the order in which they appear in the book. Look for the symbol in the book for the relevant backing track.

Where both parts of a duet are included on the CD, the top part is in the left channel, and the bottom part is in the right channel.